MW00619111

A Field Guide to

AMPHIBIANS
and REPTILES
of Maricopa County

Thomas C. Brennan
Andrew T. Holycross

Arizona Game and Fish Department
2221 W. Greenway Road • Phoenix, AZ 85023
(602) 942–3000 • azgfd.gov

Acknowledgments

This publication is the result of a collaborative agreement between the Arizona Game and Fish Department and the School of Life Sciences at Arizona State University, a partnership fostered through Partners in Amphibian and Reptile Conservation (Arizona chapter).

We would like to thank the following people for their guidance, knowledge, and assistance: Roy Averill—Murray, Randy Babb, James Badman, Bob Bezy, Moira Brennan, David E. Brown, Bill Burger, Jim Collins, Erik Enderson, Kim Field, Darrel Frost, Bob Gaulden, Tony Gill, John Gunn, Dave Hardy, Sharon Holycross, Craig Ivanyi, Charlie Painter, Roger Repp, Richard Retallick, Jim Rorabaugh, Phil Rosen, Cecil Schwalbe, Jeff Servoss, Mike Sredl, and Brian Sullivan.

Cover photo: Desert Night Lizard (*Xantusia vigilis*) by Jim Rorabaugh.

Photos contributed by (in order of number contributed): Tom Brennan, Andy Holycross, Randy Babb, Jim Rorabaugh, Erik Enderson, Bob Bezy, Kim Wismann, William Wells, Jeff Boundy, and Debbie Gibson. Artwork by Randy Babb and Tom Brennan.

Funding for this project was provided by the
Arizona Game and Fish Department Heritage Fund.

April 2005
Arizona Game and Fish Department
2221 W. Greenway Road • Phoenix, AZ 85023
(602) 942–3000 • azgfd.gov

Contents

Canyon Treefrog
Hyla arenicolor

Preface

All lengths provided for salamanders, frogs, and lizards in this guide are snout to vent length (SVL). In the amphibians, this is the distance from the tip of the snout to the opening of the vent, whereas in lizards it is measured from the tip of the snout to the posterior edge of the cloacal scute. The tail (if present) is not included in SVL measurements. Measurements for snakes are total length (tip of the snout to the tip of the tail) and shell length is provided for turtles. Measurements are provided in millimeters (mm) and inches (").

Natural and life history information provided here (*e.g.* diet, clutch sizes, mating season) is based on the authors' observations, the scientific literature, as well as general statements appearing in other field guides.

Common and scientific names used in this guide generally follow the recommendations of Crother *et al.* (2000. Herpetological Circular 29. Society for the Study of Amphibians and Reptiles) and Crother *et al.* (2003. Herpetological Review 34:196–203). However, we follow the recommendation of Douglas *et al.* (2002. Pp 11–50, *In* Biology of the Vipers. Eagle Mountain Publishing, Eagle Mountain, Utah) with regard to recognizing the Arizona Black Rattlesnake (*Crotalus cerberus*) as a full species.

Distribution maps. The maps represent the authors' best estimates of where the species can be expected in Maricopa County based on knowledge of habitat and distribution; they are not the result of an examination of all available museum specimens and should not be cited as the basis for publication of range extensions.

 Areas where a species is expected to occur (in appropriate habitat).

 Historic range, from which the species appears to be (for the most part) extirpated.

Introduction

Home to a richly varied terrain and at least eight major biomes (four of them deserts), Arizona is one of the most biologically diverse states in the country. Biotic communities range from Lower Colorado Sonoran Desertscrub flats and undulating sand dunes, through foothills of Arizona Upland Sonoran Desertscrub, Chaparral, Pinyon–Juniper Woodland, up to Montane Conifer Forest, and cool Subalpine Forest. On the peaks of the San Francisco Mountains there is even a small tract of Alpine Tundra. Arizona is further blessed with a diversity of grasslands, including Plains and Semidesert Grassland and patches of Mountain Meadow.

Located in the central part of the state, Maricopa County harbors many of these habitats. Elevation in our county ranges from near 300 meters (1,000 feet) in the flats southwest of Gila Bend to over 2,300 meters (7,600 feet) on the peaks of the Mazatzal Mountains. Over 90% of the county is blanketed in subtropical Sonoran Desert, the warmest, wettest, and most diverse of all North American deserts. The southern portion of the county is comprised primarily of Lower Colorado Sonoran Desertscrub plains characterized by creosotebush, white bursage, and small drainages lined with blue paloverde and ironwood trees. Scattered throughout this sea of creosotebush are dry, rocky mountains festooned with ocotillo, saguaro, and the odd elephant tree. Arizona Upland habitats increasingly dominate the landscape as one moves north in the county. Here, sloping bajadas and rocky hills are populated by ocotillo, jojoba, and a variety of cacti, including towering saguaro. Dry washes lush with littleleaf paloverde, mesquite, and ironwood trees wend their way, ribbon-like, through these "thornscrub" habitats. Further north and northeast lie relict patches of Semidesert Grassland. Chaparral covers the hills surrounding Seven Springs, the middle elevations of the Mazatzal and Superstition mountains, and an isolated remnant tops the Harquahala Mountains. Small stands of Montane Conifer Forest shade the high northern slopes and creekbeds of the Mazatzal and Superstition mountains.

These habitats harbor a remarkable variety of amphibians and reptiles. Perhaps most surprising to the newcomer is the presence of 14 species of frogs and toads. Lowland Burrowing Treefrogs, Sonoran Desert Toads, Great Plains Narrow-mouthed Toads, Great Plains Toads, and two spadefoot toads all reside in the lowest and hottest portions of the county, where they spend much of the year underground. The Arizona Toad, Woodhouse's Toad, and Canyon Treefrog all occupy uplands and are usually found near permanent or seasonal streams. Two species of leopard frog (one native and one introduced) are found in our perennial streams and rivers. Two turtles are native to Maricopa County. The large and terrestrial Desert Tortoise reaches its highest densities on steep boulder-strewn slopes of

Arizona Upland Sonoran Desertscrub, while Sonoran Mud Turtles dwell in the pools of permanent and seasonal streams. Spiny Softshells, Pond Sliders, and Snapping Turtles have been introduced to our man–made urban lakes and canals. Maricopa County even has a resident salamander – the Tiger Salamander whose amazing life cycle includes aquatic larvae that can develop into cannibals, terrestrial adults, or neotenes (adults in the larval form).

Thirty–one species (seven families) of lizard are found in Maricopa County, including one of only two venomous lizards in the world – the Gila Monster. Desert Iguanas, Common Chuckwallas, Zebra–tailed Lizards, Long–nosed Leopard Lizards, Side–blotched Lizards, the primordial Madrean Alligator Lizard, five whiptail lizards, three species of collared lizard, three horned lizards, three spiny lizards, two earless lizards, two skinks, two night lizards, and two ghost–like geckos (one native and one introduced) also inhabit the county. Snake diversity is no less remarkable and includes 31 species in five families. One fifth of the world's rattlesnakes (seven species) can be found in Maricopa County. Like all members of the family Viperidae, rattlesnakes are highly venomous. Sonoran Coralsnakes are also venomous and belong to the Elapidae, a family that includes cobras and kraits. Although Sonoran Coralsnakes have small mouths and rarely bite, their venom includes potent neurotoxins and they should not be handled. Most snakes in the county are harmless and belong to a diverse family known as the Colubridae. Maricopa County representatives include several tiny "sand swimmers", highly aquatic gartersnakes, large, swift, and diurnal whipsnakes, and at least two snakes that dine exclusively on the eggs of lizards and other snakes. Rear–fanged and mildly venomous (but harmless) species like the Nightsnake, Western Lyresnake, and Ring–necked Snake are also found in our county. Finally, Rosy Boas and Western Threadsnakes belong to the Boidae and Leptotyphlopidae (respectively), two families with primarily tropical associations.

Numerous parks and trail systems in the county provide opportunities to find and experience these wonderful creatures first hand. Several species may not persist in Maricopa County much longer, and some, such as the Mexican Gartersnake might already be extirpated. Pollution, land development, urban sprawl, water diversions, disease, and introduced species have significantly reduced the ranges and populations of some species. We hope that this book will foster a greater appreciation of these amazing animals and their fragile habitats. Our desert landscapes, complete with Gila Monsters, Desert Tortoises, and rattlesnakes are a significant draw in Arizona's tourism industry and contribute immeasurably to our quality of life. Prudent economic planning must include conservation of intact ecosystems. With responsible planning we can help to ensure that generations of Arizonans and tourists enjoy the amazing diversity of amphibians and reptiles that are an invaluable part of our natural heritage.

Viewing tips

Many amphibians and reptiles are conspicuous. Some species, however, are only above ground for a few nights each year and can be difficult to find. However, by considering timing, environmental conditions, search methods, and habitat, you can tip the odds of finding secretive or rare species in your favor.

Choosing the right time of the year and time of day is critical. Amphibians and reptiles are generally most active during the warmer months of the year (March through October). Many reptiles are active during the day in Spring, when temperatures are relatively mild. In summer, extremely high daytime temperatures deter diurnal surface activity and many animals become more active at twilight or during the night. Most of our frogs and toads don't surface until the summer monsoon rains, when they emerge to breed at temporary pools, often in large aggregations. To find these seemingly improbable desert denizens, drive deserted roads at night, a day or two after a rainstorm, and stop occasionally to listen for loud choruses of mating toads. The cooler temperatures of fall allow many reptiles to return to surface activity during the day. Preferred ambient temperatures vary greatly among species, but recent rains dramatically increase your chances of seeing most amphibians and many reptiles.

"Road–riding" is one of the more popular and successful methods of finding amphibians and reptiles. This practice consists of driving slowly on remote paved roads that pass through suitable habitat. The twilight hours, just before and after sunset, are especially productive, although many species can be found late into the night. Scan the roadway and shoulder for animals crossing the road or soaking up heat from the pavement. Road–riding is most effective for snakes, toads, and geckos. Most lizards, however, are easiest to observe while hiking on mild days.

Many amphibians and reptiles are heard long before they are seen. When in the field, listen for rustling in bushes or leaf litter, the rattling of disturbed gravel, or for the amorous songs of courting frogs and toads. Take time to inspect shady retreats under bushes, the trunks of trees, and in crevices. A pocket mirror is handy for shining sunlight into dark recesses where animals often retreat during the day. Don't expect to see movement, as many amphibians and reptiles remain motionless to avoid detection. Before entering an area take time to scan it with binoculars. Lizards can often be spotted basking atop distant rocks, though they often abandon these perches when approached. Likewise, scanning the opposite banks of ponds and streams allows one to spot and identify frogs or toads before they leap into the water and disappear. Many species are closely associated with specific habitats and the probability of finding them increases considerably as one becomes familiar with their favored environs. The checklist in the back of this guide will help you keep track of your observations.

A fishing license issued by the Arizona Game and Fish Department allows you to capture or possess most of Arizona's amphibians and the Spiny Softshell. A hunting license allows the capture and possession of most of our reptiles. Combination hunting/fishing licenses are also available. Use of spotlights and prying devices is prohibited. Tribal laws and regulations govern the collection of amphibians and reptiles on tribal land. Some of the animals in this book are protected throughout Arizona; the Desert Tortoise, Gila Monster, Mexican Garter Snake, and Lowland Leopard Frog may not be collected or killed. The following species do not occur in Maricopa County, but are also protected throughout Arizona, and may not be collected or killed: the Tarahumara Frog, Plains Leopard Frog, Chiricahua Leopard Frog, Northern Leopard Frog, Relict Leopard Frog, Ramsey Canyon Leopard Frog, Flat-tailed Horned Lizard, Rock Rattlesnake, Twin-spotted Rattlesnake, Ridge-nosed Rattlesnake, Milksnake (Cochise County only), Massasauga, Narrow-headed Garter Snake, and Ornate Box Turtle. Please check with the Arizona Game and Fish Department for current bag and possession limits and changes to rules and regulations.

Snakebite: Avoidance and First Aid

How dangerous are they? Rattlesnake envenomations are rarely fatal when medically treated, but do pose a serious health risk. Envenomation usually results in intense pain and swelling and can include local tissue damage, loss of digits, and/or arthritis. Gila Monsters only bite when handled, and envenomations usually result in severe pain and swelling, and sometimes infection.

Avoidance. Most snakebite "victims" are envenomated due to their own carelessness or negligence. These incidents usually involve young men who have attempted to handle, kill, provoke, or move a rattlesnake. Left unmolested, most rattlesnakes will not attempt to strike people, which they perceive as potential predators. A rattlesnake's first line of defense is to remain motionless and unnoticed. Failing this, they often rattle and assume a defensive posture. Although defensive displays are intimidating, and might *seem* aggressive, they are in fact purely defensive. Rattlesnakes sometimes crawl towards the safety of a hole or refuge when threatened, and if you are blocking their retreat, it might seem like they are "attacking". As a last resort, rattlesnakes will strike to defend themselves. One often hears that a rattlesnake can strike a distance of half of its body length. However, because determining the length of a coiled snake is difficult, and because rattlesnakes are capable of moving quickly, it is best to stay ten feet or more away from the snake. Do not push the limits. Another common question is, "What should I do if I hear a snake but don't see it?" Stop, listen, look, and locate. Once you spot the snake, move cautiously in the opposite direction. Sudden movement might provoke a strike. Snakes sometimes congregate during the mating and denning seasons. Move cautiously so that you don't step on a snake you haven't noticed.

First Aid. In the event that you or a hiking partner are struck by a snake, a list of first aid "do's and don'ts" is provided below. While this is likely to be a traumatic experience, it is critical to remain calm and get to a hospital with emergency care facilities as soon as possible.

What to do:

- First, call for assistance and/or evacuation to the nearest medical facility for treatment, even if you are unsure whether or not venom has been injected.
- Remove jewelry and constrictive clothing.
- Keep the person calm and minimize physical activity.
- If possible, the victim should lie down, with the legs slightly elevated.

What NOT to do:

- NO ice or heat.
- NO electric shock.
- NO tourniquets or "pressure bandages".
- NO incision, suction, or venom extraction devices.
- Do NOT attempt to kill or handle the rattlesnake.
- Avoid driving if possible. If no other transportation or phone is available, drive to the nearest help or phone and no further.

Banner Good Samaritan Poison Center: 602-253-3334

Toad Toxins

Toads have skin glands that secrete toxins as a defense against predators. Most toads produce mildly poisonous toxins that only irritate predators' mouths. One of our toads, the Sonoran Desert Toad, produces highly potent toxins that can be dangerous or even fatal when ingested by predators. Owners of cats and dogs should be alert to the potential for poisoning should their pet lick or bite a Sonoran Desert Toad. There is no antidote to toad toxin, so quick recognition of symptoms and help from a veterinarian can be critical. Toads pose little risk to humans who handle them, but people should wash their hands before touching their eyes, nose, and mouth.

Symptoms of poisoning (pets):
- Drooling and licking of lips.
- Pawing at mouth.
- Irregular heartbeat.
- Dazed or uncoordinated state.
- High body temperature.
- Seizures.
- Unconsciousness.
- Possible death.

Treatment:
- If pet is conscious, rinse mouth with gentle flow of water from a hose. Do not force water into the throat. Rinse from the side of the mouth out the front.
- Wet your pet's coat with water to help cool body temperature.
- Take your pet to a veterinarian immediately.

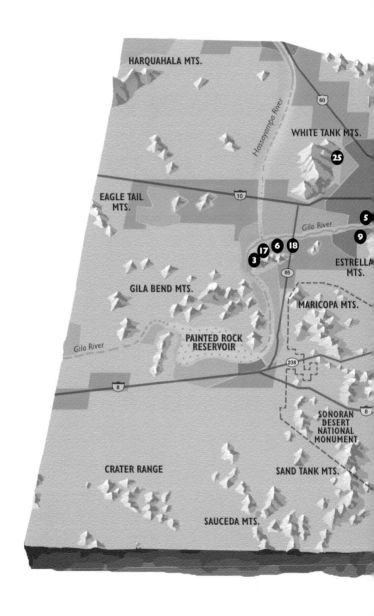

HARQUAHALA MTS.

Hassayampa River

WHITE TANK MTS.

EAGLE TAIL MTS.

Gila River

ESTRELLA MTS.

GILA BEND MTS.

MARICOPA MTS.

Gila River

PAINTED ROCK RESERVOIR

SONORAN DESERT NATIONAL MONUMENT

CRATER RANGE

SAND TANK MTS.

SAUCEDA MTS.

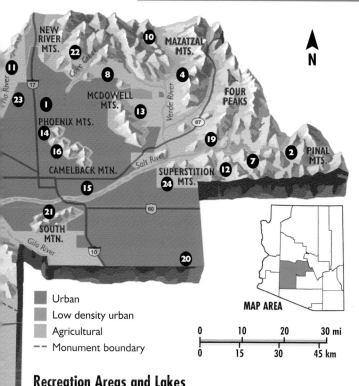

Urban
Low density urban
Agricultural
-- Monument boundary

MAP AREA

| 0 | 10 | 20 | 30 mi |
| 0 | 15 | 30 | 45 km |

Recreation Areas and Lakes

1 Adobe Dam Regional Park
2 Apache Lake
3 Arlington Wildlife Area
4 Bartlett Lake
5 Base and Meridian Wildlife Area
6 Buckeye Hills Regional Park
7 Canyon Lake
8 Cave Creek Regional Park
9 Estrella Mountain Regional Park
10 Horseshoe Lake
11 Lake Pleasant Regional Park
12 Lost Dutchman State Park
13 McDowell Mountain Regional Park
14 North Mountain Park
15 Papago Park
16 Piestewa Peak Park
17 Powers Butte Wildlife Area
18 Robbins Butte Wildlife Area
19 Saguaro Lake
20 San Tan Mountain Regional Park
21 South Mountain Park
22 Spur Cross Ranch Conservation Area
23 Thunderbird Park
24 Usery Mountain Regional Park
25 White Tank Mountain Regional Park

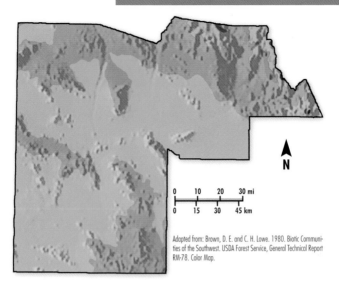

Adapted from: Brown, D. E. and C. H. Lowe. 1980. Biotic Communities of the Southwest. USDA Forest Service, General Technical Report RM-78. Color Map.

Montane Conifer Forest – Typically on high mountains (2000–3050 m or 6500–10,000'). Conspicuous plants include ponderosa pine and gambel oak. Usually above Pinyon–Juniper or Chaparral.

Pinyon–Juniper Woodland – Foothills and lower mountain slopes (1500–2300 m or 4900–7500'). Conspicuous plants include one–seed and rocky mountain juniper, pinyon, grasses, and shrubs. Often above Chaparal and below Montane Conifer Forest.

Chaparral – Foothills and mountain slopes (1505–2150 m or 3400– 7000'). Conspicuous plants include shrub live oak, mountain mahogany, and manzanita. Above Arizona Upland desertscrub, below Pinyon–Juniper Woodland or Montane Conifer Forest.

Semidesert Grassland – Flats and foothills (1100–1700 m or 3600–5600'). Conspicuous plants include curly mesquite, tobosa, and hairy grama grasses, pricklypear, mesquite, or one–seed juniper. Often above Arizona Upland Desertscrub, below Chaparral.

Sonoran Desertscrub

Arizona Upland Subdivision – Low mountains, hills, and bajadas (300–1050 m or 980–3500'). Conspicuous plants include saguaro (and other cacti), palo verde, ironwood, and jojoba. Above Lower Colorado desertscrub, often below Chaparral.

Lower Colorado Subdivision – Flatlands and low rocky mountains (300–400 m or 980–1300'). Plants include creosotebush, white bursage, and saltbush. Below Arizona Upland Desertscrub.

Facing Page: Arizona Upland Desertscrub in the Maricopa Mountains, Maricopa County, Arizona.

13

Lower Colorado Desertscrub in the Rainbow Valley, Maricopa County, Arizona.

Arizona Upland Desertscrub in the McDowell Mountains, Maricopa County, Arizona.

Semidesert Grassland on the west flank of the Mazatzal Mountains, Maricopa County, Arizona.

Chaparral in the Mazatzal Mountains, Maricopa County, Arizona.

Pinyon–Juniper Woodland in Tonto Basin, Gila County, Arizona.

Montane Conifer Forest on Mount Ord, Mazatzal Mountains, Maricopa County, Arizona.

terrestrial adult

Tiger Salamander
Ambystoma tigrinum

aquatic larva

Tiger Salamander
Ambystoma tigrinum

Tiger Salamander *Ambystoma tigrinum*

Arizona's only salamander. Large and stocky (to 165 mm or 6.5") with a rounded snout and protruding eyes. Adults are dark gray to black with greenish yellow spots, bars, or reticulations on the back and limbs. Larvae are olive–gray with three protruding gills on each side of the neck. Some larvae become cannibals and develop larger head and jaws. Adults are terrestrial, except neotenes (adults that remain in larval form). Usually found from Semidesert Grassland up to Montane Conifer Forest, but sometimes found in Arizona Upland Desertscrub. Adults spend much of their time in burrows or under surface objects near ponds, but can be found abroad during humid or rainy weather. Larvae are found in ponds, cattle tanks, lakes, and other sources of permanent or temporary water. Tiger Salamanders are carriers of chytrid fungus which can be lethal to other amphibians. Salamanders should not be moved between water sources. Feeds on a variety of invertebrates and occasionally small vertebrates. Breeds in winter and spring. Females lay from 200–2000 eggs in water. Eggs take about 3 weeks to hatch.

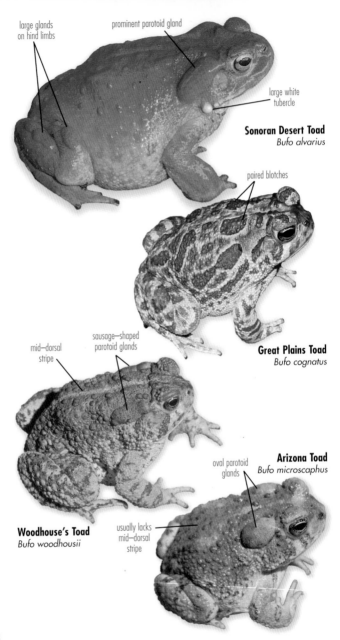

large glands on hind limbs

prominent parotoid gland

large white tubercle

Sonoran Desert Toad
Bufo alvarius

paired blotches

Great Plains Toad
Bufo cognatus

mid–dorsal stripe

sausage–shaped parotoid glands

Woodhouse's Toad
Bufo woodhousii

usually lacks mid–dorsal stripe

oval parotoid glands

Arizona Toad
Bufo microscaphus

18

Sonoran Desert Toad *Bufo alvarius*

Our largest toad (to 191 mm or 7.5"). Olive green to brown in color with smooth, but bumpy skin. Prominent parotoid glands on the sides of the head and on the hind limbs distinguish it from the Bullfrog (p. 23). Young have small dark tubercles tipped with orange. Generally a denizen of low deserts and foothills, although sometimes found high in Pinyon–Juniper Woodland. Breeds in temporary pools formed by monsoon rains. Adults are often found far from water. Eats insects and other invertebrates, lizards, small mammals, and amphibians. Exudes toxic secretions that, if ingested, can cause hallucinations, paralysis, or death in dogs and other vertebrates.

Great Plains Toad *Bufo cognatus*

A medium–sized (to 114 mm or 4.5") gray, tan, or olive toad. Dark olive blotches on the back in symmetrical pairs separated by a faint mid–dorsal stripe. Found in a variety of habitats including Lower Colorado and Arizona Upland Desertscrub, agricultural areas, Semidesert Grassland, and Chaparral. Eats insects and other invertebrates. Breeds late spring through summer, predominantly during the monsoon.

Woodhouse's Toad *Bufo woodhousii*

A medium–sized (to 127 mm or 5"), bumpy toad with a prominent light mid–dorsal stripe. Olive–gray to yellow–brown with dark irregular blotches on the back. Sausage–shaped parotoid glands. Occupies Lower Colorado and Arizona Upland Desertscrub, Semidesert Grassland, and Chaparral. Prefers permanent and semi–permanent water sources and sandy soil. Abundant along river corridors and in farmland. Eats insects and other invertebrates. Breeds in streams and pools in spring.

Arizona Toad *Bufo microscaphus*

A medium–sized (to 84 mm or 3.25"), gray toad with a rusty, olive, or yellow hue. Toadlets tend to be light olive. Large oval parotoid glands. Occasionally hybridizes with Woodhouse's Toad in Maricopa County. Usually found along rocky, shallow streams from Arizona Upland Desertscrub to high in Montane Conifer Forest. Alteration of habitat may be a threat to populations in Maricopa County. Eats a variety of invertebrates including insects. Breeds in streams in early spring.

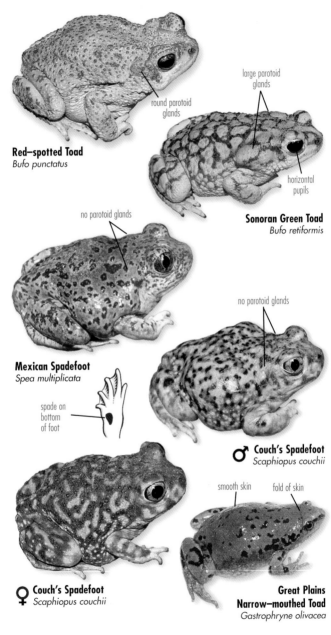

Red–spotted Toad
Bufo punctatus

round parotoid glands

large parotoid glands

horizontal pupils

Sonoran Green Toad
Bufo retiformis

no parotoid glands

Mexican Spadefoot
Spea multiplica

spade on bottom of foot

no parotoid glands

♂ **Couch's Spadefoot**
Scaphiopus couchii

♀ **Couch's Spadefoot**
Scaphiopus couchii

smooth skin

fold of skin

Great Plains Narrow–mouthed Toad
Gastrophryne olivacea

Red—spotted Toad *Bufo punctatus*

A small (to 76 mm or 3"), gray to tan toad with a flat head and numerous small red tubercles. Flat head, horizontal pupils, and round parotoid glands distinguish it from the Mexican Spadefoot. Usually found near temporary or permanent water in habitats ranging from Lower Colorado and Arizona Upland Desertscrub to Pinyon—Juniper Woodland. Eats insects and occasionally young toads. Breeds in spring or monsoon.

Sonoran Green Toad *Bufo retiformis*

A small toad (to 64 mm or 2.5") with a network of black reticulations on a yellowish green background. Flat head and sausage—shaped parotoid glands distinguish it from Couch's Spadefoot. Found in Lower Colorado and Arizona Upland Desertscrub habitats. Eats invertebrates. Breeds in temporary pools during monsoon.

Mexican Spadefoot *Spea multiplicata*

A small (to 64 mm or 2.5"), gray—green toad with dark blotches and red tubercles. Vertical pupils. Black wedge—shaped spades on hind feet and lack of parotoids distinguish it from Red—spotted Toad. Occupies Arizona Upland Desertscrub to Montane Conifer Forest. Eats insects and spiders. Breeds in temporary pools during monsoon.

Couch's Spadefoot *Scaphiopus couchii*

A medium—sized (to 89 mm or 3.5"), lime—green toad. Females tend to be boldly patterned with black reticulations. Males may be plainer, often with faint or no reticulations. Vertical pupils, black sickle—shaped spades on hind feet, and lack of parotoid glands distinguish it from Sonoran Green Toad. Found in Lower Colorado and Arizona Upland Desertscrub habitats. Common in agricultural areas. Eats invertebrates and occasionally small vertebrates. Breeds in temporary pools during summer rains.

Great Plains Narrow—mouthed Toad
Gastrophryne olivacea

A tiny (to 41 mm or 1.6"), grayish—brown amphibian with smooth skin and a pointed nose. Small and scattered dark spots and blotches are usually present on the back and limbs. Found near ephemeral pools from Lower Colorado Desertscrub to Semidesert Grassland. Feeds primarily on ants and termites. Breeds after summer rains.

Lowland Burrowing Treefrog
Pternohyla fodiens

toe pads

Canyon Treefrog
Hyla arenicolor

no dorsolateral folds

no parotoid glands

American Bullfrog
Rana catesbeiana

webbed hind feet

dorsolateral fold

**Rio Grande
Leopard Frog**
Rana berlandieri

webbed hind feet

dorsolateral fold

Lowland Leopard Frog
Rana yavapaiensis

webbed hind feet

Canyon Treefrog *Hyla arenicolor*

A small (to 57 mm or 2.25") frog with rough skin and large rounded toe pads. Usually gray or olive, often with darker gray–green blotches. Found from Arizona Upland Desertscrub into Montane Conifer Forest in rocky canyons or arroyos near permanent or temporary streams. Sometimes found in large boulder clusters or talus slopes far from water. Eats insects. Breeds from early spring through the monsoon.

Lowland Burrowing Treefrog *Pternohyla fodiens*

A small (to 64 mm or 2.5"), yellow–brown frog with red–brown blotches outlined in pale yellow. The snout is round and bill–shaped. Found in Lower Colorado Desertscrub and Semidesert Grassland in Arizona, usually near temporary pools in washes. Spends much of its life burrowed underground waiting for the summer rains. Eats insects and other invertebrates. Breeds during the monsoon rains.

American Bullfrog *Rana catesbeiana*

NON–NATIVE A large (to 203 mm or 8") frog. Olive–green with faint bands on the hind limbs. Lacks dorsolateral folds, distinguishing it from leopard frogs. Lacks parotoids, distinguishing it from Sonoran Desert Toad (p. 19). Aquatic, but travels overland. Eats almost anything it can swallow, including small vertebrates. Its introduction is a threat to aquatic ecosystems and several native species. Breeds spring to fall.

Rio Grande Leopard Frog *Rana berlandieri*

NON–NATIVE A medium–sized (to 114 mm or 4.5"), green or olive frog with dark spots, large eyes, and dorsolateral folds. Usually no spots on the snout in front of the eyes. Lives along streams, rivers, canals, and farmland ditches. Eats insects and other invertebrates. Breeds from February to November.

Lowland Leopard Frog *Rana yavapaiensis*

PROTECTED A medium–sized (to 83 mm or 3.25"), tan or olive–brown frog with darker spots and dorsolateral folds. Sometimes has spots on snout. Often smaller and browner than Rio Grande Leopard Frog. Lives in permanent water, usually along streams. Introduced Rio Grande Leopard Frog may have displaced it in the lower Salt and Gila rivers. Eats insects and other invertebrates. Breeds January through October.

high domed carapace

distinct growth lines on shell

Desert Tortoise
Gopherus agassizii

projections under chin

Sonora Mud Turtle
Kinosternon sonoriense

red patch

Pond Slider
Trachemys scripta

spiked tail

leathery shell

Snapping Turtle
Chelydra serpentina

snorkel–like snout

Spiny Softshell
Apalone spinifera

24

Desert Tortoise *Gopherus agassizii*

PROTECTED A large (to 381 mm or 15") land turtle with a gray to brown domed shell and stocky limbs. Lives in naturally occurring rock shelters or self–created burrows in habitats ranging from Arizona Upland Desertscrub to lower Chaparral. Eats grass, herbs, and other plants. Lays a clutch of 1–12 eggs in spring or summer.

Sonora Mud Turtle *Kinosternon sonoriense*

A small (to 165 mm or 6.5") turtle with a brown to olive shell, distinct light and dark markings on the sides of the head and neck, and fleshy projections under the chin. Lives in rocky streams, creeks, or ponds in habitats ranging from Arizona Upland Desertscrub to Montane Conifer Forest. Usually found in or near water. Eats insects, snails, fish, frogs, and plants. Lays clutches of 1–11 eggs in spring and summer.

Pond Slider *Trachemys scripta*

NON–NATIVE A medium–sized (to 355 mm or 14") turtle with a yellow and olive streaked shell and a wide orange–red patch on each side of the head. Introduced to urban ponds, lakes, and parts of the lower Gila River. Eats plants, insects, crayfish, snails, tadpoles, and fish. Lays clutches of up to 25 eggs in spring and summer.

Snapping Turtle *Chelydra serpentina*

NON–NATIVE A large (to 457 mm or 18") aquatic turtle with sharp hooked jaws and a long spiked tail. Black to olive–brown. Introduced to urban lakes and canals. Eats crayfish, snails, insects, fish, waterfowl, and other vertebrates. Lays from 8 to over 100 eggs in spring or summer. Bites are capable of inflicting serious injury.

Spiny Softshell *Apalone spinifera*

NON–NATIVE A flat turtle with a leathery carapace, growing to 533 mm (21"). Brown to olive, occasionally with spots or flecks. Snout is pointed and protruding. Lives in permanent lakes, slow–moving rivers, and canals. Eats worms, snails, crayfish, insects, fish, frogs, and plants. Lays up to 39 eggs in spring or summer.

25

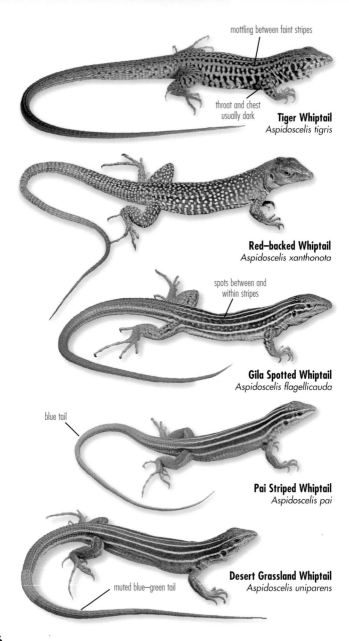

mottling between faint stripes

throat and chest usually dark

Tiger Whiptail
Aspidoscelis tigris

Red–backed Whiptail
Aspidoscelis xanthonota

spots between and within stripes

Gila Spotted Whiptail
Aspidoscelis flagellicauda

blue tail

Pai Striped Whiptail
Aspidoscelis pai

muted blue–green tail

Desert Grassland Whiptail
Aspidoscelis uniparens

Tiger Whiptail *Aspidoscelis tigris*

A medium–sized (to 127 mm or 5"), slim, orange–brown lizard with a long tail and dark mottling. Faint stripes sometimes present on the back. Active during the day in Lower Colorado Desertscrub through Chaparral. Eats insects, spiders, and lizards. One or more clutches of 1–4 eggs are laid in spring and summer.

Red–backed Whiptail *Aspidoscelis xanthonota*

A medium–sized (to 127 mm or 5"), slim lizard with an orange–red back and a long thin tail. Light spots or blotches on the back and sides. Sides of the head and legs are often bluish. Usually found in canyons in Arizona Upland Desertscrub and Semidesert Grassland. Eats insects and spiders. Lays 2–10 eggs in summer.

Gila Spotted Whiptail *Aspidoscelis flagellicauda*

A slim, medium–sized (to 95 mm or 3.75"), brown lizard with a long tail and 6 yellow stripes on the back. Light spots on the back between and within stripes. Diurnal. Found from Semidesert Grassland through Montane Conifer Forest. Eats insects and spiders. All are female (parthenogenetic). Lays 2–6 eggs in June or July.

Pai Striped Whiptail *Aspidoscelis pai*

A small (to 76 mm or 3"), slim, reddish brown lizard with 6 light yellow stripes (no spots) on the back. The face, feet, tail, and under-side are pale blue. Active during the day in Chaparral and Montane Conifer Forest in eastern Maricopa County. Eats insects and spiders. Clutches of 1–3 eggs are laid in late spring or summer.

Desert Grassland Whiptail *Aspidoscelis uniparens*

A slim, small (to 83 mm or 3.25"), dark brown lizard with 6 or 7 light stripes on the back. The long, thin tail is muted blue, turquoise, or brown. Found during the day in low hills and flat areas in Semidesert Grassland and Chaparral. Eats insects and other invertebrates. All are female (parthenogenetic). Two or more clutches of 1–4 eggs laid in spring and early summer.

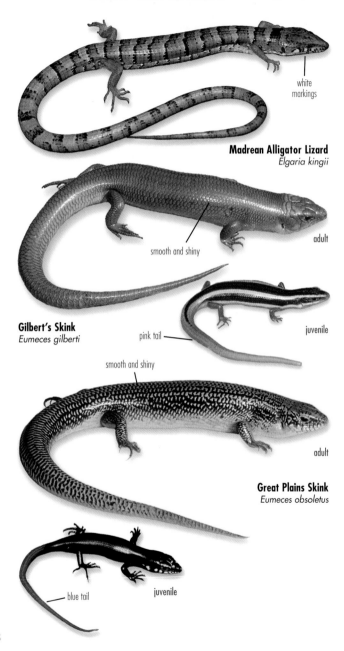

white markings

Madrean Alligator Lizard
Elgaria kingii

smooth and shiny

adult

Gilbert's Skink
Eumeces gilberti

pink tail

juvenile

smooth and shiny

adult

Great Plains Skink
Eumeces obsoletus

blue tail

juvenile

Madrean Alligator Lizard *Elgaria kingii*

A medium—sized (to 140 mm or 5.5"), long—bodied lizard with relatively small limbs and a long, thick tail. Shiny rectangular scales on back and belly. Creamy tan body marked by crossbars of reddish brown with dark edges. Crisp white markings on sides of the face. Young are usually darker and more prominently marked than adults. Found in northeastern Maricopa County in Semidesert Grassland, Chaparral, and Montane Conifer Forest.

Active during the day and evening, this ground dweller is often found under cover of leaf litter, rock piles, rat nests, fallen logs, dead plants, and pine needles. Seems to be most abundant in wooded canyons or along drainages. Eats insects, spiders, and scorpions. Mates in spring and lays 9—15 eggs in summer.

Gilbert's Skink *Eumeces gilberti*

A medium—sized (to 114 mm or 4.5"), shiny gray, tan, or olive lizard with relatively small limbs and a thick tail. Some adults have red or orange coloration on the head and tail. Young have light and dark striping on the body and pink tails. Found in habitats ranging from Arizona Upland Desertscrub through Chaparral in northwestern Maricopa County. A secretive lizard that spends most of its time under rocks, leaf litter, and logs near moist riparian areas, canyons, or on moist north—facing steep slopes. Eats insects and spiders. Lays a clutch of 3—9 eggs in summer.

Great Plains Skink *Eumeces obsoletus*

A medium—sized (to 133 mm or 5.25"), shiny, tan, gray, or olive lizard with a dark net—like pattern created by dark crescents on the rear edges of the scales. Limbs are relatively small and the tail is thick. Young are solid black with bright blue tails and prominent white spots on the sides of the face. In Maricopa County it is found in Semidesert Grassland, Chaparral, Pinyon—Juniper Woodland, and lower reaches of Montane Conifer Forest. A secretive lizard that spends most of its time under the cover of rocks, logs, and leaf litter. Eats insects, spiders, snails, and small lizards. Lays a clutch of 7—24 eggs in spring or summer.

no tubercles

moveable eyelids

no toe pads

Western Banded Gecko
Coleonyx variegatus

tubercles on back

no eyelids

toe pads

Mediterranean House Gecko
Hemidactylus turcicus

no eyelids

Bezy's Night Lizard
Xantusia bezyi

no eyelids

Desert Night Lizard
Xantusia vigilis

Western Banded Gecko *Coleonyx variegatus*

A small (to 76 mm or 3"), peach or pinkish tan lizard with dark reddish brown crossbars or reticulations. Skin is soft, translucent, and covered in small, granular scales. Vertical pupils. Tail plump and banded. Moveable eyelids, lack of tubercles, and lack of toe pads distinguish it from the Mediterranean House Gecko. Lives in Lower Colorado Desertscrub, Arizona Upland Desertscrub, and Semidesert Grassland. May squeak when handled. An almost exclusively nocturnal ground dweller that eats insects, spiders, and other invertebrates. Lays one or more clutches of 1–2 eggs in spring and summer.

Mediterranean House Gecko *Hemidactylus turcicus*

NON–NATIVE A small (to 57 mm or 2.25"), peach or light pinkish tan lizard with reticulations or crossbars and translucent skin. Vertical pupils. Whitish tubercles on the back, prominent toe pads, and lidless eyes distinguish these geckos from the Western Banded Gecko. Introduced to urban areas. Commonly seen at night near lights on the exterior walls of buildings. Eats insects and other invertebrates. Often squeaks when captured. One or more clutches of 1–2 eggs are laid in spring and summer.

Bezy's Night Lizard *Xantusia bezyi*

A small (to 70 mm or 2.75") olive–brown to yellow–brown lizard with dark blotches or spots on the back and tail. Scales on the back are small and granular. The lidless eyes are orange to red with vertical pupils. The head and body are somewhat flattened. Found in habitats ranging from Arizona Upland Desertscrub into Chaparral and Pinyon–Juniper Woodland. These lizards are secretive crevice dwellers that are rarely seen away from the safety of large rock outcroppings and boulder piles during the day. Eats insects and spiders. Gives birth to 1–3 young in summer.

Desert Night Lizard *Xantusia vigilis*

A small (to 57 mm or 2.25"), olive–gray to yellow–brown lizard with dark flecks or speckles on the back and tail. The scales on the back are small and granular. Lidless eyes with vertical pupils. Habitat ranges from Arizona Upland Desertscrub through Chaparral. Usually found under plant debris such as dead agave plants and prickly pear cactus. These secretive lizards rarely emerge from cover during the day. Eats insects, spiders, and other invertebrates. Gives birth to 1–3 young in summer.

Long–tailed Brush Lizard
Urosaurus graciosus

tail about twice as long as body

Ornate Tree Lizard
Urosaurus ornatus

tail about as long as body

Common Side–blotched Lizard
Uta stansburiana

ear opening

single side blotch

32

Long–tailed Brush Lizard *Urosaurus graciosus*

A small (to 57 mm or 2.25"), pale gray to light brown lizard with dark gray crossbars on the back. The long tail of this lizard (up to twice the body length) distinguishes it from the shorter–tailed Ornate Tree Lizard. Habitat in Maricopa County consists of Lower Colorado and Arizona Upland Desertscrub, usually along washes. Frequents branches of trees and bushes where it is well camouflaged. When threatened these lizards often align themselves with a branch or root and remain motionless to avoid detection. Active during the warm daytime hours. Eats insects, spiders, and other invertebrates. Lays 2–10 eggs in spring or summer.

Ornate Tree Lizard *Urosaurus ornatus*

One of our most common lizards. A small (to 57 mm or 2.25"), gray or tan lizard with dark gray or brown bars on the back. The tail is usually about as long as the body, distinguishing it from the Long–tailed Brush Lizard. Found in Lower Colorado and Arizona Upland Desertscrub, Semidesert Grassland, Chaparral, and Montane Conifer Forest. Active during the day, this lizard is often seen on backyard fences and exterior walls in urban areas. Natural habitat includes boulders, rock outcroppings, and trees. Eats insects, spiders, and other invertebrates. In urban settings, eggs are often laid in moist areas such as in water meter boxes, compost heaps, or under debris piles. Lays multiple clutches of 2–16 eggs each in spring and summer.

Common Side–blotched Lizard *Uta stansburiana*

A small (to 57 mm or 2.25"), gray to orangish tan lizard with a single dark blue to black blotch on each side of the body just behind the front limbs. Dorsal markings are variable and can include no pattern, brown blotches, partial striations, chevron–like crossbars, or spots. Males often have bright turquoise–blue speckles on the upper surfaces of the back and tail. The external ear opening and single blotch on each side of this lizard distinguish it from the Common Lesser Earless Lizard (p. 35). Found in Lower Colorado Desertscrub, Arizona Upland Desertscrub, Semidesert Grassland, and Chaparral. This lizard is often seen on the ground under bushes and along the edges of washes, but is also encountered on rocks, cliff faces, boulder piles, or outcroppings. Active year round at low elevations throughout the Maricopa county. Eats insects, scorpions, and spiders. Multiple clutches of 1–8 eggs are laid in spring and summer.

Zebra–tailed Lizard
Callisaurus draconoides

ear
opening

bars near front legs

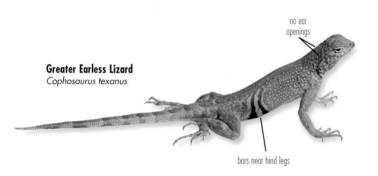

no ear
openings

Greater Earless Lizard
Cophosaurus texanus

bars near hind legs

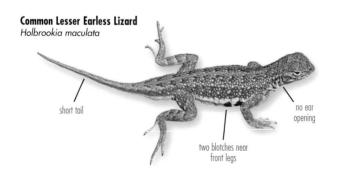

Common Lesser Earless Lizard
Holbrookia maculata

short tail

no ear
opening

two blotches near
front legs

Zebra–tailed Lizard *Callisaurus draconoides*

A medium–sized (to 102 mm or 4") lizard with a flattened tail and long thin limbs. Yellow to tan body with two dark bars extending upward from the belly just behind the forelimbs. Prominent black bars cross the white underside of the tail. External ear openings and forward position of side bars distinguish it from the Greater Earless Lizard. Found in both Sonoran Desertscrub subdivisions. Prefers flatlands and broad, sandy washes in areas with sparse vegetation. These ground dwellers flee predators with explosive bursts of speed, usually running with the tail curled over the back. Between bursts, they wag their curled tails exposing the "zebra–striped" underside. Almost exclusively diurnal, although sometimes encountered asleep on the surface at night. Eats insects, spiders, and small lizards. One or more clutches of 1–15 eggs are laid in summer.

Greater Earless Lizard *Cophosaurus texanus*

A medium–sized (to 89 mm or 3.5"), yellow, tan, or gray lizard with a flattened tail and long thin limbs. Markings consist of peach, orange, or salmon spots on the front part of the back fading into yellow on the rear portion of the back. Two dark bars extend upward from the belly just in front of the hind legs. Position of side bars and lack of external ear openings distinguish it from the Zebra–tailed Lizard. A fast–running ground dweller that is found above the flats in Arizona Upland Desertscrub, Semidesert Grassland, and Chaparral communities. Prefers sandy washes and open, rocky areas within mountainous terrain. When fleeing, this speedy lizard sometimes curls its tail over its back, exposing prominent white and black crossbars on the underside. Unlike the Zebra–tailed Lizard, these lizards rarely tail–wag. Almost exclusively diurnal. Eats insects, spiders, and other invertebrates. Lays 2–9 eggs in spring or summer.

Common Lesser Earless Lizard *Holbrookia maculata*

A small (to 64 mm or 2.5") lizard with a short tail and no external ear openings. Gray, tan, or orangish in color, often matching the color of the soil. Spots and rows of chevron–shaped blotches line the back. Underside of tail is plain white, distinguishing it from the Zebra–tailed Lizard and the Greater Earless Lizard. Two small dark bars immediately behind the forelimbs distinguish it from Common Side–blotched Lizard (p. 33). In Maricopa County this lizard is found in Semidesert Grassland and Chaparral communities. These diurnal ground dwellers are usually observed in relatively open and sparsely vegetated areas. Eats insects, spiders, and other small lizards. Lays one or two clutches of 1–10 eggs in spring and summer.

light stripe
on top of tail

dark throat
on males

Great Basin Collared Lizard
Crotaphytus bicinctores

dark groin
on males

tail taller than
it is wide

faint
crossbars

rounded tail
with no stripe

Eastern Collared Lizard
Crotaphytus collaris

large light
spots on back

Sonoran Collared Lizard
Crotaphytus nebrius

rounded tail
with no stripe

small light
spots on sides

spots and light bars

long round tail

Long–nosed Leopard Lizard
Gambelia wislizenii

Great Basin Collared Lizard *Crotaphytus bicinctores*

A medium–sized (to 108 mm or 4.25"), plump lizard with a large head and two black collars on the neck. Gray–tan to brown with light dots and alternating orange and gray–brown crossbands. Tail is higher than wide with a pale stripe running down the top. Males have dark patches on the throat and groin. Gravid females have orange bars on the sides. Found in Arizona Upland Desertscrub. Often seen basking atop large rocks or rock piles near drainages or on hillsides. Collared lizards have powerful jaws, which they use to capture invertebrates, lizards, and other small vertebrates. Occasionally eats plant material. Lays 3–7 eggs in spring or early summer.

Eastern Collared Lizard *Crotaphytus collaris*

A medium–sized (to 108 mm or 4.25"), plump lizard with a large head and two black collars on the neck. Gray–green to blue–green with yellow on the top of the head, snout, and front feet. The body has dark and light crossbars and light spots. The tail is round in cross–section. Gravid females have orange bars on the sides. Found from Arizona Upland Desertscrub through Pinyon–Juniper Woodland. Frequently seen on top of large rocks or rock piles. This lizard has powerful jaws, which it uses to capture smaller lizards and insects. Lays 1–14 eggs in spring or summer.

Sonoran Collared Lizard *Crotaphytus nebrius*

A medium–sized (to 108 mm or 4.25"), plump lizard with a large head and two black collar markings on the neck. Brown to yellow–brown with conspicuous large light spots on the back that become smaller on the sides. Tail is round in cross section. Gravid females have orange bars on sides. Typically found on rocky bajadas and hillsides in Lower Colorado and Arizona Upland Desertscrub. Eats invertebrates and smaller lizards. Lays eggs in spring or summer.

Long–nosed Leopard Lizard *Gambelia wislizenii*

A large (to 140 mm or 5.5") lizard with an elongated head and a long, rounded tail. Can change its color from light yellow–tan with dark spots, to darker gray–brown with thin lace–like lines across the back and tail. Females have orange markings on the sides, head, and under the tail in spring breeding season. Found in both Sonoran Desertscrub subdivisions and Semidesert Grassland. Frequents flat, open areas with low bushes. Aggressive hunters that eat invertebrates, lizards, snakes, small mammals, and occasionally plant material. Clutches of up to 11 eggs are laid in spring and summer.

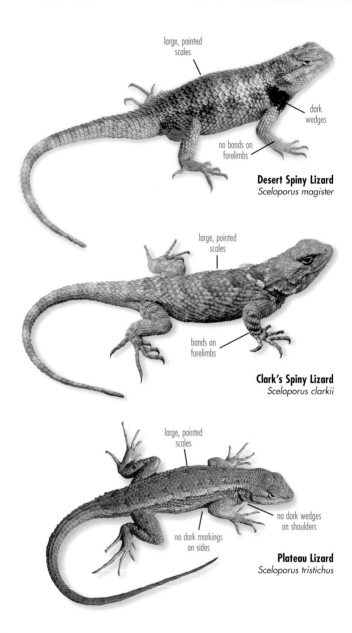

large, pointed
scales

dark
wedges

no bands on
forelimbs

Desert Spiny Lizard
Sceloporus magister

large, pointed
scales

bands on
forelimbs

Clark's Spiny Lizard
Sceloporus clarkii

large, pointed
scales

no dark wedges
on shoulders

no dark markings
on sides

Plateau Lizard
Sceloporus tristichus

Desert Spiny Lizard *Sceloporus magister*

A medium–sized (to 133 mm or 5.25"), heavy bodied lizard with large, pointed, overlapping scales on the back. Color is usually light tan, light gray–brown, or yellowish. Large dark wedges on the shoulders. Some males have a purplish back and blue–green throat. Similar to Clark's Spiny Lizard, but lacks bars on forelimbs. Ranges from Lower Colorado Desertscrub, through Pinyon–Juniper Woodland. Often seen on trunks of large trees, on packrat nests, and among large boulder or rock piles. When encountered, this lizard will usually flee into crevices or to the opposite side of a tree trunk, climbing up and out of reach. Almost exclusively diurnal. Eats insects, spiders, centipedes, other lizards, and plant material. Lays 4–19 eggs in spring or summer.

Clark's Spiny Lizard *Sceloporus clarkii*

A medium–sized (to 133 mm or 5.25"), stout lizard with pointed, overlapping scales on the back. Usually blue–gray to sooty gray with muted and irregular crossbars on the back. There is usually a dark wedge–shaped blotch on each shoulder. Dark gray or black bars on the forelimbs distinguish it from the Desert Spiny Lizard. Ranges from high elevation Arizona Upland Desertscrub into Pinyon–Juniper Woodland. A diurnal lizard usually observed on trees, but also found in large rock piles. Almost always flees to the opposite side of the tree trunk when encountered. Eats insects and occasionally plant material. Lays one or two clutches of up to 24 eggs each in spring or summer.

Plateau Lizard *Sceloporus tristichus*

A medium–sized (to 83 mm or 3.25"), brown, gray, or orange–brown lizard with pointed overlapping scales and two muted light stripes running down the sides of its back. Chevron–shaped bars or blotches between the light stripes. Unlike the other *Sceloporus* in Maricopa County, this lizard does not have dark wedges on its shoulders. Males usually have two blue patches on the throat. Lack of side–blotches distinguishes it from Common Side–blotched Lizard and Common Lesser Earless Lizard. Occupies Chaparral, Semidesert Grassland, Pinyon–Juniper Woodland, and Montane Conifer Forest. A diurnal lizard found on the ground, logs, trees, or rocks. Eats insects, spiders, snails, and other lizards. Lays one or more clutches of 4–17 eggs in spring and summer.

tail taller than it is wide

row of enlarged scales down middle of back

small blunt head

Desert Iguana
Dipsosaurus dorsalis

red–backed phase

black–backed phase

Common Chuckwalla
Sauromalus ater

bead like scales

blunt head

plump tail

Gila Monster
Heloderma suspectum

40

Desert Iguana *Dipsosaurus dorsalis*

A large (to 146 mm or 5.75"), cream to tan lizard with stocky limbs and a blunt head. Markings usually consist of white dots within a network of red–brown reticulations. Red–brown spots form bands on the tail. A single row of enlarged, pointed scales runs down the midline of the back. Most abundant in Lower Colorado Desertscrub, but sometimes found in Arizona Upland Desertscrub. Active on hot days, even when many other lizards are under cover. A ground dweller that will occasionally climb to reach the small yellow flowers of the creosote bush. Primarily herbivorous, but also eats insects and occasionally carrion. Lays up to 8 eggs in late spring or summer.

Common Chuckwalla *Sauromalus ater*

A large (to 229 mm or 9"), flat, wide, and heavy lizard with loose, baggy skin on the sides of the body and neck. Females are usually gray with faint crossbars. Males have black heads and limbs and light colored tails. Males in the south–central and southeastern portions of the county have black backs, whereas males in the north and western portions have red backs. Young are banded. Pattern and absence of large bead–like scales distinguishes it from the Gila Monster. Found in Arizona Upland Desertscrub. Common Chuckwallas are crevice dwellers that are usually observed on large rock outcroppings. When threatened, they usually retreat into a crevice and inflate themselves so that they become securely wedged. Primarily herbivorous but occasionally eats insects. Lays a clutch of up to 16 eggs in late spring or summer.

Gila Monster *Heloderma suspectum*

VENOMOUS • PROTECTED One of only two venomous lizards in the world. A very large (to 356 mm or 14"), plump lizard with a short, fat tail and hard, round, bead–like scales on the upper surfaces. Black and orangish yellow (or pinkish yellow) reticulations and bands adorn the back. The tail is marked with usually three or four large black bands on an orangish background. Sides of face and snout are usually black. Habitats range from Arizona Upland Desertscrub to Chaparral. Diurnal in spring, mostly nocturnal mid– to late summer. Spends the majority of its life underground in burrows, packrat nests, or rock crevices. Surface activity may be confined to a total of only a few weeks each year. Venom is secreted by glands in the lower jaw and delivered via grooves in the teeth by chewing. The bite is extremely painful but rarely if ever fatal. These slow lizards are typically harmless unless handled. An efficient nest raider, it feeds on small mammals, birds, eggs, lizards, and carrion. Lays a clutch of up to 12 eggs in summer.

large gap
separating horns

Greater Short–horned Lizard
Phrynosoma hernandesi

bases of horns
do not touch

Desert Horned Lizard
Phrynosoma platyrhinos

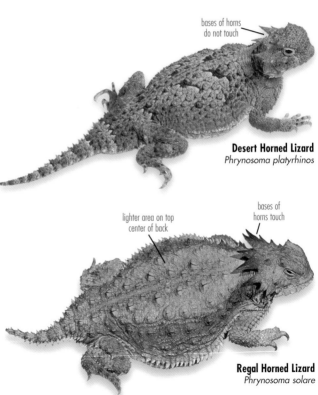

lighter area on top
center of back

bases of
horns touch

Regal Horned Lizard
Phrynosoma solare

42

Greater Short-horned Lizard *Phrynosoma hernandesi*

A medium–sized (to 121 mm or 4.75"), exceptionally flat, broad lizard with short horn–like scales projecting from the back of the head. A single row of pointed protruding scales fringe the lower sides of the body, with small spike–like scales scattered across the back. A tan, reddish–brown, or gray body often closely matches the soil on which the animal lives. Two large dark blotches on the sides of the neck. Found at higher elevations in habitats ranging from Semidesert Grassland to Montane Conifer Forest. A ground dweller that usually remains motionless when encountered, relying on crypsis to escape the notice of potential predators. Ants comprise the bulk of its diet but it also eats other invertebrates. Young born in summer.

Desert Horned Lizard *Phrynosoma platyrhinos*

A medium–sized (to 95 mm or 3.75"), exceptionally flat, and broad lizard with long spike–like scales protruding from the back of the head. Isolated pointed scales project from the back and a single row of pointed scales fringe the lower sides of the body. Gray–brown to tan in color, with highlights of orange or peach along the lower edges of the body. Color often matches the soil on which the animal lives. There are sometimes a pair of dark blotches on the neck and smaller dark blotches adorn the back. Found in Lower Colorado Desertscrub and Arizona Upland Desertscrub. Frequents open sandy areas with sparse vegetation. More likely to run than most horned lizards, although they often stop after a short sprint. Primarily eats ants, but also other invertebrates and rarely, plant material. Lays one or two clutches of up to 16 eggs in spring and early summer.

Regal Horned Lizard *Phrynosoma solare*

A medium–sized (to 121 mm or 4.75"), wide, and exceptionally flat lizard with a crown of long horns radiating from the sides and back of the head. Smaller pointed scales protrude from the back and a single row of pointed scales fringe the lower edge of the body. Gray–brown, orange–brown, or gray, often with a purplish cast. Color generally matches the soil on which it lives and is lighter and more vibrant in the middle of the back. A faint mid–dorsal stripe is sometimes present. There are usually two soft–edged dark blotches on the top of the neck. Found in Arizona Upland Desertscrub and low elevation Semidesert Grassland habitat on rocky bajadas and gently sloping hillsides. This lizard will occasionally squirt blood from its eyes when captured. Primarily eats ants but also other invertebrates. Lays a clutch of up to 33 eggs in summer.

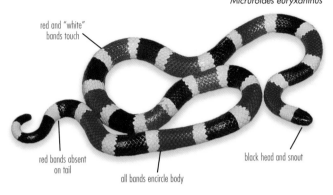

Sonoran Coralsnake
Micruroides euryxanthus

red and "white" bands touch

red bands absent on tail

all bands encircle body

black head and snout

orange background

Variable Sandsnake
Chilomeniscus stramineus

light snout

no red bands/saddles

red and "white" bands touch

light snout

Western Shovel–nosed Snake
Chionactis occipitalis

Sonoran Coralsnake *Micruroides euryxanthus*

VENOMOUS A small (to 615 mm or 24"), but long and uniformly thin snake. Red, black, and off–white to yellowish bands encircle the body. Patches of black mottling are sometimes present in the red bands. Found in habitats ranging from Lower Colorado and Arizona Upland Desertscrub, through Semidesert Grassland. Primarily nocturnal but sometimes found out on mild days. These docile snakes rarely attempt to bite, but are venomous and should not be handled. Defensive behaviors include hiding the head within the coils, presenting the tail as a "false head", writhing, and forcefully everting the vent to produce a popping noise. Consumes small snakes, such as threadsnakes, groundsnakes, shovel–nosed snakes, black–headed snakes, and nightsnakes. Threadsnakes appear to be a preferred food. Might occasionally consume small lizards. Lays 2–3 eggs during the rainy season (July–August).

Variable Sandsnake *Chilomeniscus stramineus*

A short (to 285 mm or 11") and somewhat stout snake with 19 to 49 dark saddles on an orange and cream background. Tail is relatively short. Black bands encircle the tail but not the body. Belly is pale white to cream. Small eyes, nasal valves, an inset jaw, and a flattened, spade–like snout are adaptations for burrowing and "swimming" through sand and organic debris. Primarily a denizen of Arizona Upland Desertscrub habitats, but is also found along drainages above and below this community. Usually found in or near washes and other areas with fine to coarse sand or leaf litter. Primarily crepuscular and nocturnal. Eats centipedes, native roaches, ants and their pupae and other invertebrates. Probably mates in spring and lays 2–4 eggs in June and July.

Western Shovel–nosed Snake *Chionactis occipitalis*

A small (to 369 mm or 15") snake with 21+ black bands or saddles on a light yellowish cream background. Black bands encircle the tail and posterior belly. The narrow orange–red saddles are sometimes flecked with black. Flattened snout, countersunk jaw, nasal valves, and concave belly are adaptations for locomotion in sandy environs. Often found in association with washes in Lower Colorado Desertscrub. Further south, this snake reaches high densities in and around dunes. Primarily crepuscular, but can be found throughout the night and on mild days. Eats a variety of invertebrates, including native roaches, scorpions, beetle larvae, fly larvae, ants, solpugids, spiders, as well as reptile eggs. Males fight for access to receptive females. Lays eggs in late spring and summer.

white
bands widen
toward belly

Common Kingsnake
Lampropeltis getula

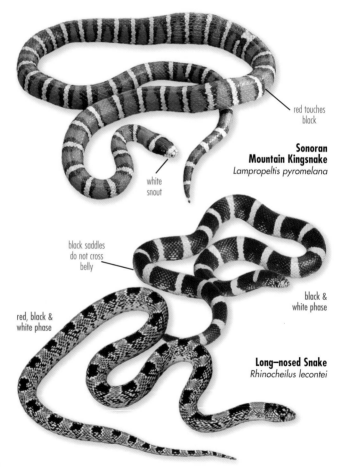

red touches
black

**Sonoran
Mountain Kingsnake**
Lampropeltis pyromelana

white
snout

black saddles
do not cross
belly

black &
white phase

red, black &
white phase

Long–nosed Snake
Rhinocheilus lecontei

Common Kingsnake *Lampropeltis getula*

A large (to 1422 mm or 56"), black snake with narrow white or yellowish bands that widen on the lower sides. Occupies Lower Colorado and Arizona Upland Desertscrub, farmland, and Semidesert Grassland. Primarily nocturnal but occasionally abroad on overcast or mild days. Of variable disposition, these snakes will sometimes exude musk when handled. A powerful constrictor with a broad diet consisting of snakes (including rattlesnakes), lizards, small mammals, nestling and adult birds, and perhaps frogs and toads. Mates in spring and lays 2–24 (usually 5–9) eggs in late June or July. Hatchlings begin to appear in late August.

Sonoran Mountain Kingsnake
Lampropeltis pyromelana

A medium–sized (to 1088 mm or 43") snake with alternating red, black, and white bands. The black bands often widen and sometimes merge together dorsally. The snout is usually white or creamy gray. Occurs in the mountains of northeastern Maricopa County in Chaparral, Pinyon–Juniper Woodland, and Montane Conifer Forest. Most often found in rocky areas with abundant leaf litter and canopy cover. Primarily diurnal but occasionally found out at night. These beautiful snakes often writhe, bite, and exude musk in response to handling. Strong constrictors, they consume lizards, rodents, birds, and rarely bats. Proficient at raiding bird nests. Clutches of 2–9 eggs are laid in June and early July and hatchlings appear in July and August.

Long–nosed Snake *Rhinocheilus lecontei*

A medium–sized (to 892 mm or 35") and lean snake with a highly variable pattern. Black saddles on the back are ringed by a thin white line and often marked with white speckles on the sides of the body. Spaces between the saddles are white, yellowish cream, pink, or red and are often flecked with black. The belly is typically cream with some speckling. Found in Lower Colorado and Arizona Upland Desertscrub, farmland, Semidesert Grassland, and Chaparral. Primarily crepuscular and nocturnal. When handled they often writhe and sometimes evert the vent, releasing blood and waste to repel would–be predators. Whiptail lizards (*Aspidoscelis*) comprise about half of this constrictor's diet, but it also eats a variety of other lizards, lizard eggs, snake eggs, and small mammals. Lays 4–11 eggs in June and July. Hatchlings appear in late August.

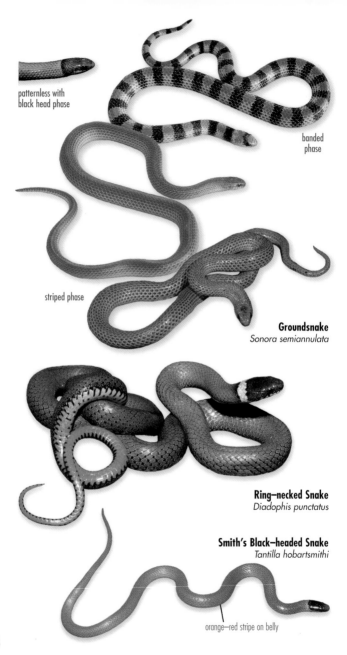

patternless with
black head phase

banded
phase

striped phase

Groundsnake
Sonora semiannulata

Ring-necked Snake
Diadophis punctatus

Smith's Black-headed Snake
Tantilla hobartsmithi

orange–red stripe on belly

Groundsnake *Sonora semiannulata*

A small (to 483 mm or 19") snake with highly variable pattern. Ground coloration may be tan, creamy gray, or orange. Patterns include black crossbands or saddles, an orange mid–dorsal stripe, and plain. In Maricopa County, some patternless Groundsnakes have a dark cap on the head and are easily confused with black–headed snakes. However, Groundsnakes lack a red stripe on the belly. Occupies a wide variety of habitats ranging from Lower Colorado Desertscrub through Pinyon–Juniper Woodland, but appears to reach its highest densities in Arizona Upland Desertscrub and Semidesert Grassland habitats. Often found in back yards and vacant lots in urbanized areas. Can be found abroad both day and night. Eats insects, spiders, scorpions, and centipedes. It appears to lay eggs in June and males fight for access to receptive females.

Ring–necked Snake *Diadophis punctatus*

A small, but long (to 857 mm or 34"), and uniformly thin snake. Bluish gray to steel gray on the back. A pale orange or yellow ring often (but not always) encircles the neck. The underside grades from yellowish orange near the head to bright red below the tail, with small black spots throughout. Occupies Arizona Upland Desertscrub, Semidesert Grassland, and Chaparral habitats. Usually encountered in the morning or near dusk. Eats other snakes and lizards including gartersnakes, skinks, and alligator lizards. Mildly venomous. Lays eggs, probably in June or July.

Smith's Black–headed Snake *Tantilla hobartsmithi*

A small (to 313 mm or 12"), light brown, gray, or tan snake with a black or nearly black head. Light red, orange, or pinkish stripe down the center of the belly distinguishes this snake from Groundsnakes. Present in a wide variety of habitats including Arizona Upland Desertscrub, Chaparral, and Pinyon–Juniper Woodland, but is most abundant in Chaparral, Semidesert Grassland and cottonwood–willow associations, where it can reach high densities. Spends most of its time underground or under rocks. Occasionally observed crossing roads at night. Eats insects, scorpions, and centipedes. Specimens from Arizona have laid eggs in August.

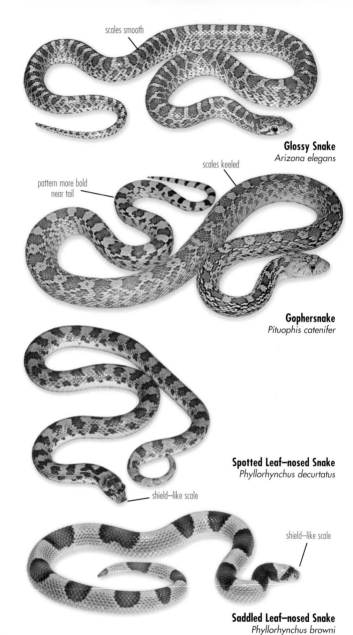

scales smooth

Glossy Snake
Arizona elegans

scales keeled

pattern more bold
near tail

Gophersnake
Pituophis catenifer

Spotted Leaf–nosed Snake
Phyllorhynchus decurtatus

shield–like scale

shield–like scale

Saddled Leaf–nosed Snake
Phyllorhynchus browni

Glossy Snake *Arizona elegans*

A medium–sized (to 1055 mm or 42") snake with tan or gray blotches on a yellowish cream or faded tan background. Pale belly with no markings. Occupies Lower Colorado and Arizona Upland Desertscrub, through Semidesert Grassland. A good burrower, it is often found in open areas of shrubby desert with sandy or loamy soil. Primarily nocturnal but sometimes found during the day. This constrictor consumes lizards, snakes, and small rodents. Mates in spring. Lays 2–16 eggs in late June and early July.

Gophersnake *Pituophis catenifer*

A long (to 2337 mm or 92") and muscular snake. Tan, cream, or yellow with rusty brown dorsal blotches and smaller markings laterally. The pale belly is usually marked with small dark blocks. Occupies a broad array of habitats and can be encountered anywhere in Maricopa County. Most abundant below about 6,500' (1981 m). Often abroad on mild days, but nocturnal during hot weather. Common in the diet of several raptors. Some hiss loudly and strike when encountered, but others are calm and gentle. This brawny constrictor feeds on rodents, lizards, snakes, and raids bird nests. Mates in spring. Lays 2–24 eggs in June and July, and hatchlings start to appear in August.

Spotted Leaf–nosed Snake *Phyllorhynchus decurtatus*

A small (to 510 mm or 20"), light tan or cream–colored snake with more than 17 small brown blotches on the back. Pale belly with no markings. Found in both Sonoran Desertscrub subdivisions, usually on alluvial soils and bajadas. Appears to occupy slightly rockier habitats than Saddled Leaf–nosed Snake. A shield–like scale on the nose aids in excavating lizard nests. Often observed at night during the hot, dry part of the summer. Less frequently encountered at other times of the year. In the wild, this specialist feeds only on the eggs of lizards and snakes. Lays 2–6 eggs in summer.

Saddled Leaf–nosed Snake *Phyllorhynchus browni*

A small (to 508 mm or 20") light tan or cream colored snake with fewer than than 17 brown saddles on the back. Pale belly with no markings. Found primarily in Arizona Upland Desertscrub in association with alluvial soils and bajadas. A shield–like scale on the nose probably aids in excavating lizard nests. Active at night during the hot, dry part of the summer, and infrequently encountered in other seasons. In the wild, this specialist feeds only on the eggs of lizards and snakes. Lays 2–6 eggs in summer.

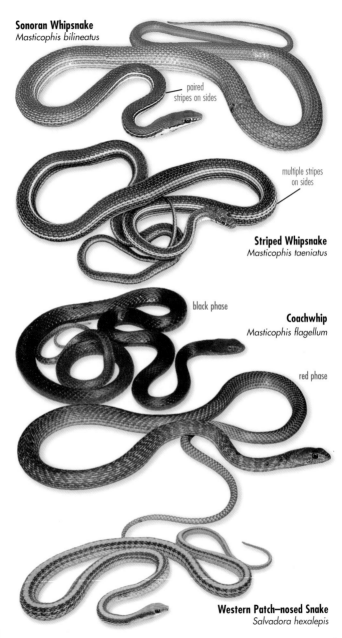

Sonoran Whipsnake
Masticophis bilineatus

paired stripes on sides

multiple stripes on sides

Striped Whipsnake
Masticophis taeniatus

black phase

Coachwhip
Masticophis flagellum

red phase

Western Patch–nosed Snake
Salvadora hexalepis

Sonoran Whipsnake *Masticophis bilineatus*

A long (up to 1778 mm or 70"), bluish green or olive–brown snake with two or three white or cream stripes on each side that fade posteriorly. The belly is usually creamy white and yellowish under the tail. Found in Arizona Upland Desertscrub foothills and mountains, Semidesert Grassland, Chaparral, and Pinyon–Juniper Woodland. This alert and fast–moving diurnal snake is a good climber and often seen cruising through the branches of trees and bushes. Eats lizards, other snakes, small mammals, birds, and frogs. Mating has been observed in June. Lays eggs in June and July.

Striped Whipsnake *Masticophis taeniatus*

A long (up to 1652 mm or 65"), grayish green to olive–brown snake with multiple white to cream stripes on the sides that are bisected by thin (often dashed) black lines. The underside is creamy yellow and usually coral pink or reddish under the tail. Found in Semidesert Grassland, Chaparral, and Pinyon–Juniper Woodland, and infrequently in Arizona Upland Desertscrub. Diurnal, fast moving, and alert. Eats lizards, snakes, small mammals, birds, frogs, and insects. Lays eggs in June and July.

Coachwhip *Masticophis flagellum*

A long (up to 1728 mm or 68"), graceful serpent of variable color. Most are pinkish red, tan, or rust above. Some individuals are solid black above, while others are only black on part of the body. The underside is usually pinkish white and reddish under the tail. Abundant in both Sonoran Desertscrub subdivisions, it is also sometimes encountered in Chaparral and Pinyon–Juniper Woodland. Diurnal, fast, and excep-tionally alert. One of the most versatile predators in the Sonoran Desert, this snake hunts during the day for lizards, snakes (including rattlesnakes), rodents, bats, birds, nestlings, frogs, toads, small tur-tles, insects, and carrion. Lays eggs in summer.

Western Patch–nosed Snake *Salvadora hexalepis*

A medium–sized (1014 mm or 40"), tan snake with two thick, dark stripes down the back and two thinner dark lines on each side. Pale cream belly. The large scale covering the snout protrudes slightly on the sides. Found on bajadas, rolling foothills, washes, and mountains from Lower Colorado Desertscrub into Chaparral, and Pinyon–Juniper Woodland. Diurnal, fast, and alert. It feeds on reptile eggs, lizards, and small mammals. Lays 4–12 eggs in summer.

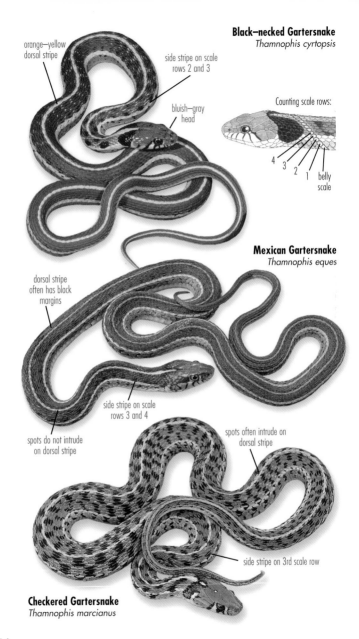

Black-necked Gartersnake
Thamnophis cyrtopsis

orange–yellow dorsal stripe

side stripe on scale rows 2 and 3

bluish–gray head

Counting scale rows:

4 3 2 1 belly scale

Mexican Gartersnake
Thamnophis eques

dorsal stripe often has black margins

side stripe on scale rows 3 and 4

spots do not intrude on dorsal stripe

spots often intrude on dorsal stripe

side stripe on 3rd scale row

Checkered Gartersnake
Thamnophis marcianus

54

Black–necked Gartersnake *Thamnophis cyrtopsis*

A medium–sized (up to 1070 mm or 42"), olive–green snake with an orange–yellow stripe down the middle of the back and light cream side–stripes on the 2nd and 3rd scale rows. Black spots between the stripes. Bluish gray head with two conspicuous, crescent–shaped black blotches on neck. Light gray and unmarked belly. Usually found near water in canyons or semi–permanent streams, but occasionally found far from water. Ranges from Arizona Upland Desertscrub, through Chaparral, Pinyon–Juniper Woodland, into Montane Conifer Forest. Active day and night depending on conditions. Eats frogs, toads, tadpoles, lizards, and invertebrates. Young are born late June and July.

Mexican Gartersnake *Thamnophis eques*

PROTECTED A medium–sized (up to 1120 mm or 44"), rust or olive–brown snake with a single cream mid–dorsal stripe. On the anterior part of the body the side–stripes are on the 3rd and 4th scale rows. Small black markings between the stripes. If present, black marks on neck are diffuse. Pale below. Found in and near streams in habitats ranging from Sonoran Desertscrub through Semidesert Grassland, into Chaparral. Once found along the Salt and Gila rivers, this species appears to be extirpated from Maricopa County, but might still occur in the Agua Fria River on the border with Yavapai County. Primarily diurnal. Eats frogs, toads, tadpoles, fish, invertebrates, and sometimes lizards and small mammals. Young are born June through early July.

Checkered Gartersnake *Thamnophis marcianus*

A medium–sized (up to 1088 mm or 43"), olive–green snake with a yellow stripe down the middle of the back. Light cream side–stripes only on the 3rd scale row. Black spots appear in a checkerboard pattern between these stripes. Olive–green head with two conspicuous, brown blotches ringed in black on neck. Light creamy gray below. In Maricopa County this snake is found in Lower Colorado Desertscrub and may be expanding its range in association with the spread of agriculture. Seems to prefer the vicinity of ponds, tanks, and river basins, but is sometimes found far from water. Active day and night. Eats frogs, toads, fish, lizards, invertebrates, and probably small mammals. Young are born late June through July.

Desert Rosy Boa

Rosy Boa
Lichanura trivirgata

Mexican Rosy Boa

dark collar

smooth
and shiny

Night Snake
Hypsiglena torquata

terminal
spine

Western Threadsnake
Leptotyphlops humilis

lyre–shaped
marking on head

**Western
Lyresnake**
Trimorphodon biscutatus

Rosy Boa *Lichanura trivirgata*

A medium–sized (up to 950 mm or 37"), heavy bodied snake with a blunt tail. Three wide stripes on a cream or grayish tan background. Two subspecies occur in the county; in one the stripes are black (or nearly so) and in the other they are rusty orange. Pale cream below with dark spots or blotches. Primarily nocturnal but often active during morning or early evening. Found from Arizona Upland Desertscrub through Chaparral, usually on or near rocky mountains or hillsides. A powerful constrictor that preys primarily on mammal and bird nestlings. Captives have given birth October to November.

Nightsnake *Hypsiglena torquata*

A small (up to 598 mm or 23"), gray snake with dark brownish gray blotches. Usually has a dark "collar" on the neck consisting of one, two, or three blotches. Vertical pupils. Pale belly with no markings. Found in an extremely wide variety of habitats ranging from Lower Colorado Desertscrub, through Arizona Upland Desertscrub, and Pinyon–Juniper Woodland, to Montane Conifer Forest. Crepuscular and nocturnal. Primarily consumes lizards, snakes and their eggs, but also frogs, toads, insects, and possibly scorpions. Mildly venomous. Lays an average of 3 or 4 eggs in June or July.

Western Threadsnake *Leptotyphlops humilis*

A small (up to 389 mm or 15") snake that superficially resembles a shiny, thin earthworm. Both head and tail are blunt and the tail has a small terminal spine. Eyes are only dark dots beneath the scales. Pinkish or mauve in color with a silvery sheen. Found in habitats ranging from Lower Colorado Desertscrub to Chaparral. Primarily nocturnal. This snake spends most of its time underground. Feeds mainly on adult and larval ants and termites, but also consumes other insects (mainly larvae), centipedes, millipedes, whipscorpions, and spiders. Lays 2–6 eggs from July to August.

Western Lyresnake *Trimorphodon biscutatus*

A medium–sized (up to 1026 mm or 40"), gray snake with darker orangish brown hollow blotches on the back. A prominent lyre–shaped marking adorns the top of the triangular head. Vertical pupils. Usually found in rocky foothills and on mountain slopes in habitats ranging from Arizona Upland Desertscrub through Pinyon–Juniper Woodland. Primarily nocturnal. Injects mild venom with enlarged rear teeth and also capable of constricting prey. Eats lizards, rodents, bats, and birds. Lays 7–20 eggs.

57

black and white bands **roughly** equal in length

Western Diamond–backed Rattlesnake
Crotalus atrox

Mojave Rattlesnake
Crotalus scutulatus

black tail bands **usually** narrower than white bands

black tail

Black–tailed Rattlesnake
Crotalus molossus

horn–like scales above eyes

Sidewinder
Crotalus cerastes

Western Diamond–backed Rattlesnake *Crotalus atrox*

VENOMOUS Arizona's largest rattlesnake (up to 1676 mm or 66"). Gray to tan with "salt and pepper" flecking throughout and brown diamond–shaped blotches on the back. Black and white bands on the tail are usually roughly equal in width. Eye stripe crosses the side of face forward of the corner of the mouth. Found from creosote flats into Pinyon–Juniper Woodland but most abundant in Arizona Upland Desertscrub. Hibernates alone or in small groups. Abroad at night and on mild days. Eats small mammals, lizards, and birds. Two to 16 young born during the monsoon.

Mojave Rattlesnake *Crotalus scutulatus*

VENOMOUS A large rattlesnake (up to 1270 mm or 50"). Green, gray, or tan with a series of dark brown diamond or rectangular blotches (usually ringed in black and yellow-ish cream). "Salt and pepper" flecking absent. Black bands are usually narrower than white bands on the tail. Eye stripe crosses the lip behind the corner of the mouth. Found in Lower Colorado and Arizona Upland Desertscrub and Semidesert Grassland. Primarily nocturnal, but also out on mild days. Feeds mostly on small mammals, but also eats birds, lizards, frogs, and toads. Young feed more heavily on lizards. Mates March and April and again during the monsoon. Young are born during the monsoon.

Black–tailed Rattlesnake *Crotalus molossus*

VENOMOUS A large (up to 1219 mm or 48"), olive–green or yellow–green rattlesnake. The back has large dark blotches with a few light green scales within their margins. Black tail, or nearly so. A generalist that occurs in habitats ranging from Arizona Upland Desertscrub through Montane Conifer Forest. Usually found in mountainous terrain. Active around the clock when conditions are favorable. Eats small mammals, including rabbits. Young are born during the monsoon season.

Sidewinder *Crotalus cerastes*

VENOMOUS A small (up to 628 mm or 25"), tan rattlesnake with brown blotches. Light spaces between the dark blotches. Scales above the eyes are raised and horn–like. Almost always found in flat, open desert with sandy or loamy soil. Most abundant near dunes and on creosote flats. Primarily nocturnal, but often active during the day in spring and fall. Their unique method of moving across sandy soil (sidewinding) leaves easily identifiable J–shaped tracks. Feeds extensively on lizards and small mammals, but also takes birds and snakes. Young are born during the monsoon season.

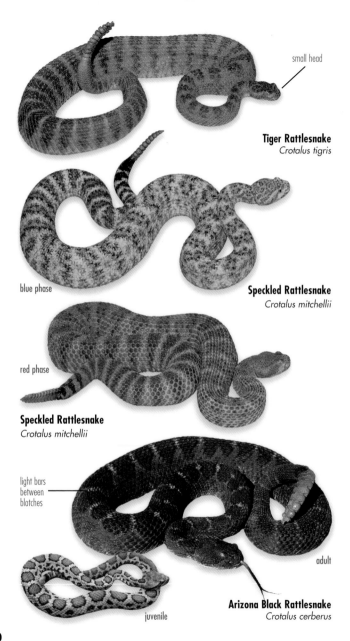

small head

Tiger Rattlesnake
Crotalus tigris

blue phase

Speckled Rattlesnake
Crotalus mitchellii

red phase

Speckled Rattlesnake
Crotalus mitchellii

light bars
between
blotches

adult

juvenile

Arizona Black Rattlesnake
Crotalus cerberus

60

Tiger Rattlesnake *Crotalus tigris*

VENOMOUS A medium–sized (up to 885 mm or 35"), blue–gray to orange–red rattlesnake. Peach or orange suffusion often present on sides. Dark and sometimes diffuse bands on the back with limited speckling. Often confused with Speckled Rattlesnakes, Tiger Rattlesnakes have a much smaller head relative to their body size. Found primarily in Arizona Upland Desertscrub foothills and mountains, but ranges into Chaparral and Pinyon–Juniper Woodland. Infrequently encountered in desert flats near hills or mountains. Primarily nocturnal, but often found abroad on mild days. Eats small mammals and lizards. Mating and births occur during the monsoon season.

Speckled Rattlesnake *Crotalus mitchellii*

VENOMOUS A large (up to 1295 mm or 51"), bluish gray, grayish white, peach, or reddish rattlesnake. Coloration sometimes matches the soil and rocks of its habitat. Speckling on the back forms diffuse blotches that resemble bands toward the tail. Sometimes prominently banded. Small black and white bands often present on tip of tail. In Maricopa County this snake is found on bajadas and mountains in rocky and boulder strewn Arizona Upland Desertscrub habitat. Primarily nocturnal, but also found out on mild days. Eats small mammals, birds, and lizards. Mates in spring and young are born during the monsoon.

Arizona Black Rattlesnake *Crotalus cerberus*

VENOMOUS A large (up to 1062 mm or 42"), dark gray to nearly solid black rattlesnake with black blotches. Spaces between the blotches form yellowish or white crossbars. Young are light gray or tan, with prominent dark blotches and facial markings. Primarily a denizen of Chaparral, Pinyon–Juniper Woodland, and Montane Conifer Forest, but sometimes found in Semidesert Grassland and canyons in higher portions of Arizona Upland Desertscrub. Active day or night, when conditions are favorable. Eats small mammals, lizards, and birds. Young born during the monsoon.

Glossary

adaptations: behavioral, physiological, or anatomical characteristics of organisms that confer fitness advantages, traits that have or will spread through populations via natural or indirect selection

alluvial: pertaining to clay, silt, sand, gravel, or similar material deposited by running water

anterior: situated forward, toward the front end of a body

aquatic: living principally in water

arroyo: a usually dry watercourse or creekbed in an arid region

bajada: gently sloping, conjoined masses of alluvial gravel, sand, and earth that extend from mountain bases out into the surrounding valley

bask: to lie in or expose oneself to warmth or sunshine

biotic community: a group of interdependent organisms inhabiting the same region and interacting with each other.

bisected: divided into two equal parts

camouflaged: concealed or disguised, usually via crypsis

cannibals: species that eat their own kind

carapace: dorsal part of the shell of a turtle consisting typically of symmetrically placed bones overlaid by horny plates

carrion: dead and putrefied or dried animal flesh

chevron: a shape consisting of two diagonal stripes meeting at an angle ⋀

chytrid: an unusual group of aquatic fungi that are either decomposers or parasites of invertebrates; a new species, *Batrachochytrium dendrobatidis,* infects the skin of amphibians, is associated with amphibian declines, and is the first chytrid found to infect vertebrates

cloaca: the common pouch into which the urinary, intestinal and reproductive organs discharge in birds, reptiles, amphibians, and many fishes

cloacal scute: The large scale (sometimes divided) that covers the vent of the cloaca

clutch: a nest of eggs

concave: hollowed inward, like the inside of a bowl

constrictor: a animal that subdues its prey by squeezing it to death

crepuscular: active around sunrise and sunset

cross–section: a cutting at a right angle to the main axis of a body

crypsis: a color, pattern, body shape, or behavior that results in an organism blending into its environment

denizen: inhabitant, resident

disposition: an animal's prevailing temperament or behavioral tendencies

distribution: the geographical range of an organism

diurnal: active during the day

docile: calm, easily controlled

dorsal: pertaining to the back of an animal

dorsolateral folds: fleshy ridges of skin that run down both sides of back

ecosystem: a dynamic and interrelating complex of plant and animal communities and their associated non–living environment

envenomation: injection of venom (which does not necessarily happen every time a venomous animal bites or strikes)

ephemeral: temporary, lasting only a short time

evert: to turn outward or "inside out"

excavate: to dig out and remove, as dirt from a burrow

external: on the outside

extirpated: completely removed from a predefined area, locally extinct

exude: to ooze or pass gradually out of a body structure

fatal: lethal, causing death

forelimbs: the two limbs closest to the head of an animal

generalist: an animal whose habits or habitats are varied or unspecialized

gills: respiratory organs used to obtain oxygen from water

glands: a cluster of cells that secrete liquid or viscous products, often organized in the form of prominent aggregations or as small organs

gravid: full of eggs, pregnant

groin: the juncture of the lower abdomen and the inner part of the thigh

habitat: the environment where a plant or animal naturally or normally lives and grows

hatchlings: recently hatched animals

herbivorous: subsisting on plants for food

hybrid: an offspring of two animals of different species

hybridizes: interbreeds and produces hybrids

ingest: to take in for food, swallow

invertebrate: animal that lacks a spinal column

keeled: scales with a ridge ("keel") running down their length

larva: a form of an animal that at birth or hatching is unlike the parent and must metamorphose before assuming the adult form

larvae: plural of larva

lateral: relating to, or situated on, the sides

lyre: a stringed harp used by the ancient Greeks

mid—dorsal: in the middle of the back

monsoon: in Arizona, the summer season characterized by increased humidity and rainfall, often in the form of thundershowers, usually lasting from early July through mid—September

musk: a substance with a penetrating persistent odor excreted from the cloacal region

nasal valves: flaps in the nares that prevents debris from entering the nose when closed

neotenes: animals that attain adulthood in the larval form

nocturnal: active at night

non—native: not naturally present in an area; introduced

parotoid glands: paired, puffy skin glands located on the rear aspect of the head of most bufonid toads and some hylid frogs that secrete chemicals that are toxic or irritating to potential predators

parthenogenetic: reproduces by development of an egg to form a zygote, without fusion of its nucleus with a male gamete; an asexual form of reproduction that results in all—female clonal lineages

perennial: present at all seasons of the year

plastron: ventral part of the shell of a turtle consisting typically of symmetrically placed bones overlaid by horny plates

posterior: situated behind, the back end of the body

primordial: of or relating to the earliest ages

pupae: an intermediate, immobile stage of a metamorphic insect (for example, bee, moth, or beetle) that occurs between the larval and adult forms

raptors: a bird of prey (*e.g.* hawks, eagles, and falcons)

reticulations: a pattern consisting of two or more networked or interlaced colors

riparian: an habitat that is transitional between land and water ecosystems, usually with vegetation reflecting the influence of water

saddles: colored markings on the back of an animal that extend onto the sides but do not encircle the body

scales: small, flat, rigid, and definitely circumscribed skin folds forming part of the external body

secrete: to release some sort of liquid substance

solpugids: arachnids with large fangs and a segmented abdomen

spade: horny, dark projections on the hind feet of some toads that aid in burrowing backward into the soil

species: roughly, a "kind" of organism. More accurately, a population of organisms, distinguishable from other populations, in having shared individual characteristics and in terms of evolutionary relatedness

specimen: an individual, considered typical of a group

striations: parallel stripes or lines

subspecies: a geographic subset of a species wherein the organisms appear slightly different from other organisms of the same species in other geographic regions

terminal: occurring at the tip or end of something

terrestrial: living principally on the ground or on land

toe pads: expanded areas on the tips of the digits of some frogs that aid in adhesion to vertical or upside down surfaces

translucent: permitting the passage of diffuse light

tubercle: a small knobby prominence or bump on an animal

vegetation: the plant growth forms that generally occupy a given area

venom: a toxic secretion that is actively delivered to the target organism, often injected by fangs or stingers

venomous: possesses glands for the secretion of venom

vent: the external opening of the cloaca

ventral: pertaining to the belly or underside of an animal

vertebrate: animals that possess a spinal column (*e.g.* fish, amphibians, reptiles, birds, mammals)

Glossary definitions adapted (in part) from:

Lees, Richard. Biology-Online.org. 2005. Online Biology Dictionary. http://www.biology-online.org/dictionary.asp Accessed 2005 February 23.

Mirriam—Webster. 2005. Mirriam—Webster OnLine Dictionary. http://www.m-w.com/ Accessed 2005 February 23.

Checklist/Index

Salamanders 17

Frogs & Toads 19

Turtles 25

Lizards 27

Snakes 45